BRAIN BOOSTERS

SUPER-SMART PUZZLES

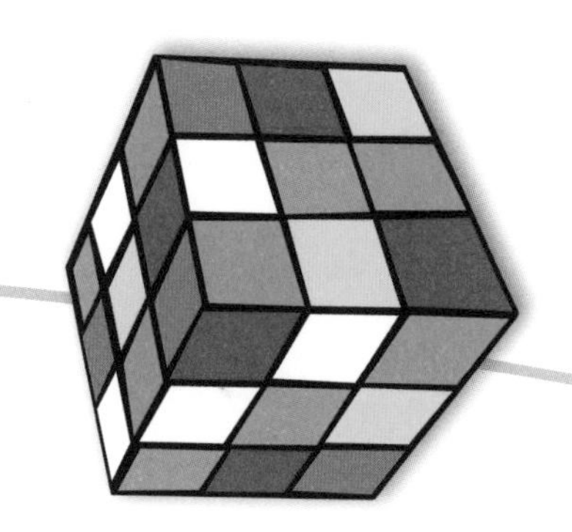

This edition published in 2018 by Arcturus Publishing Limited
26/27 Bickels Yard, 151–153 Bermondsey Street,
London SE1 3HA

ISBN: 978-1-78428-349-0
CH005338NT
Supplier 29, Date 0118, Print run 6693

Edited by Kate Overy and Joe Harris
Written by Kate Overy
Illustrated by Ed Myer and Graham Rich
Designed by Trudi Webb

Printed in China

TIPS ON LOGIC PUZZLES FROM WISE OWL

Here are some helpful hints from Wise Old Owl to get you off to a great start.

Your first challenge will be to figure out what you need to do to solve each puzzle.

Read the introduction to each puzzle carefully. You can find useful clues in the words we have used.

Look for patterns in picture, number, and letter sequences... It may help to read them aloud or write them in a line.

If you are confused by a puzzle, leave it to one side and come back to it later. You can use the answers at the back if you're totally stuck. Have fun!

WISE OLD OWL'S LIBRARY

Owl loves to read. Look at the books and figure out what the missing cover should look like.

ROBOTS RULE!

These robots all do the same job. Figure out what that is and fill in the blanks.

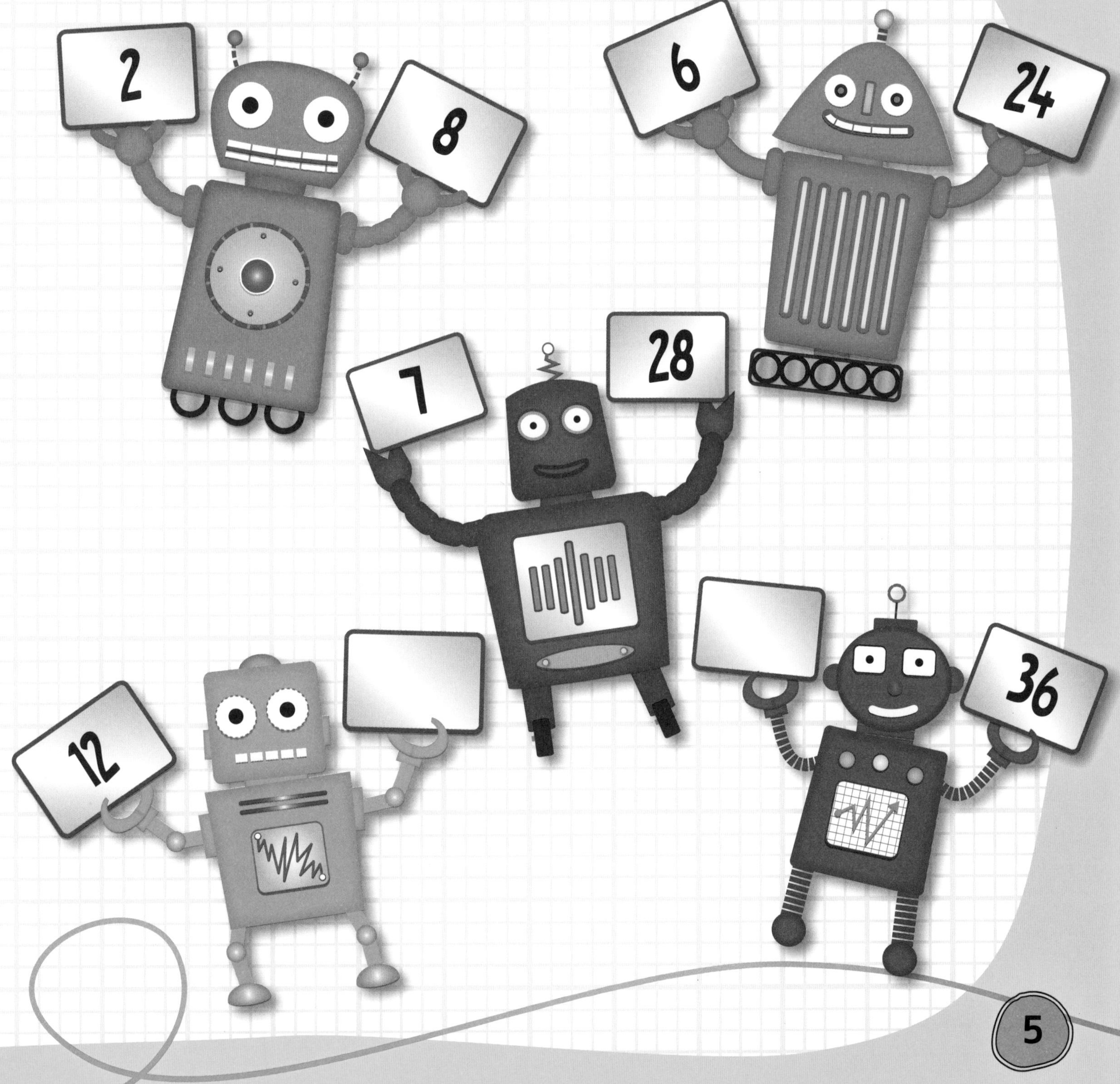

BREAKFAST BRAIN TRAINING

Start your day with brain food! Can you connect all of the cereal hoops with only four straight lines, without taking your pen or pencil off the page until you finish?

The Odd Alien

Look at all the aliens and their spaceships. Which one is the odd one out?

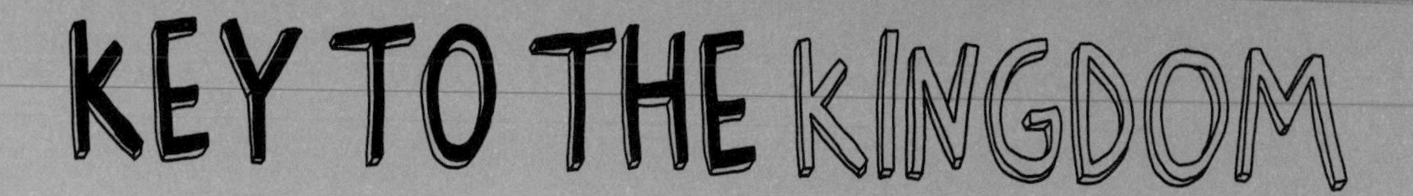

KEY TO THE KINGDOM

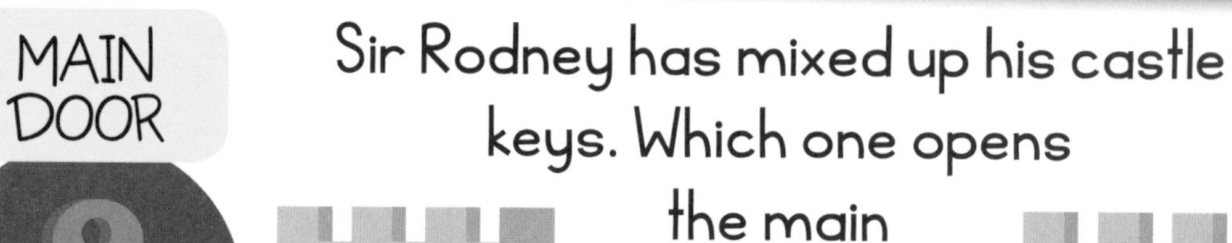

Sir Rodney has mixed up his castle keys. Which one opens the main castle door?

SHIFTING SHIELDS

Something is happening to these shields. Can you shade in the last one correctly?

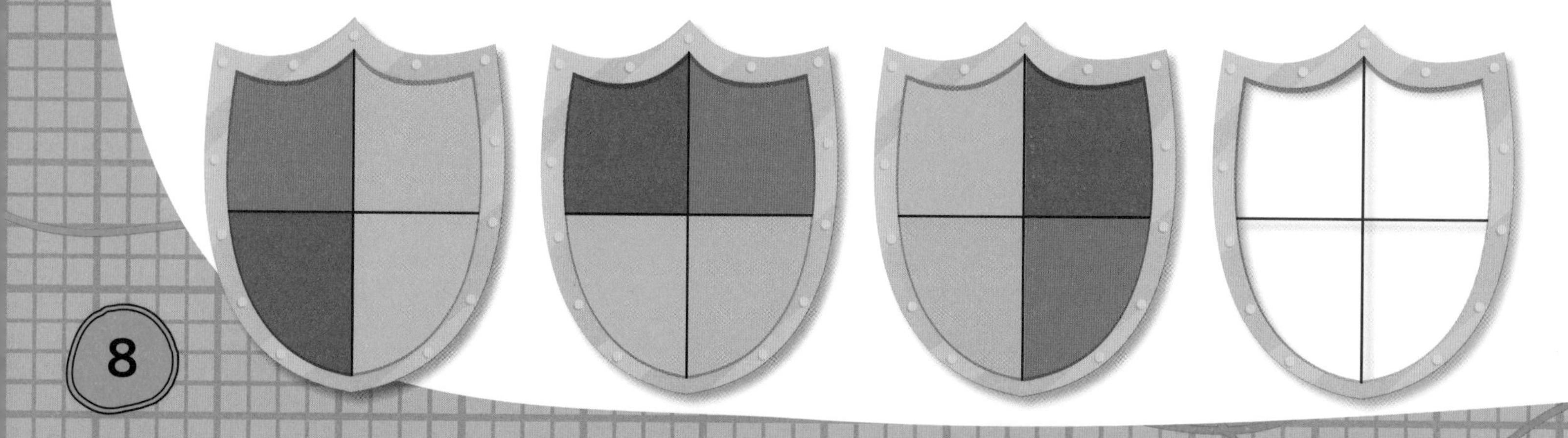

DOUBLE TROUBLE

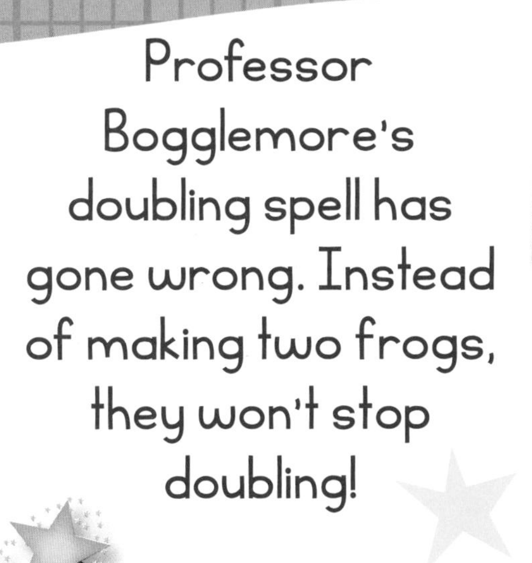

Professor Bogglemore's doubling spell has gone wrong. Instead of making two frogs, they won't stop doubling!

Every minute the frogs double in number. In 60 minutes the frogs have completely filled the wizard's box.

To the nearest minute, how much time was needed to half-fill the box?

The Wild West

Four cowboys live above places in their town. Figure out where each one lives by reading the clues below.

1. Bronco Bill lives directly between Cactus Jack and Curly Pete.
2. Cactus Jack lives above the Sheriff.
3. Giddy-Up Gill doesn't live above the Bank.

CACTUS JACK'S TRIP

Cactus Jack rode into town on Friday, stayed for three days, and left on Friday. How did he do it?

WHAT TO WEAR?

Each letter represents an item of clothing. What should Captain Cutlass wear on deck today?

MIND-BENDING MATCHSTICKS

Here are a couple of fun matchstick puzzles for you. How quickly can you figure them out?

Remove six matchsticks to leave three triangles. They don't have to be equal in size.

Move two sticks to make three triangles, all equal in size.

PYRAMID PUZZLE

Figure out the number pattern on the pyramid and fill in the missing blocks.

Pharaoh's Secret

Tim has found a secret coded message written on an ancient tomb. Use the code below to discover the Pharaoh's secret!

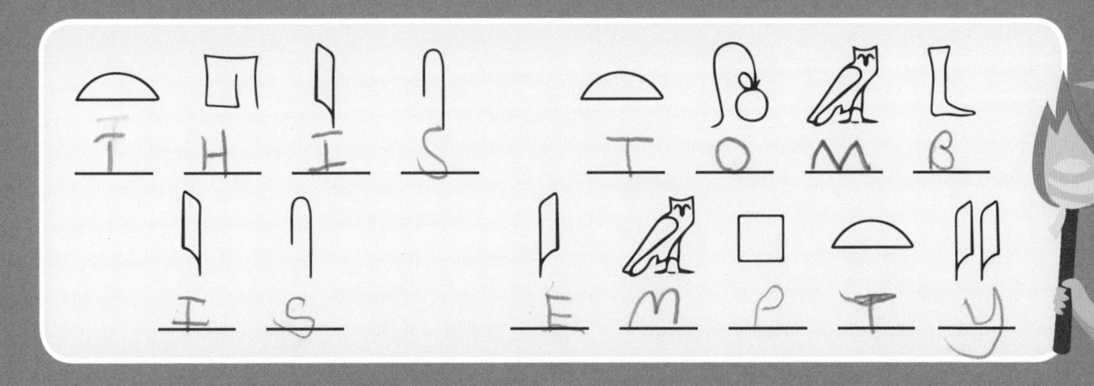

TIME TO RUN!

Burglar Bea has grabbed the last bag of gold bars from the bank's safe. As she is making her getaway she sees herself in the mirror. Time to run!

Which of the three reflections shown is the one Bea saw in the mirror?

Split It!

Burglar Bea now has to share the 60 gold bars she stole with the rest of her gang.

Burglar Bea gets 30 bars

Light-Fingered Louis gets 10% of the bars.

Robber Rick gets 1/4 of the bars

How much is left for Baby-Faced Bob?

NIGHT SHIFT

Look at the buildings on Freddie Fox's street. The lights in the windows follow a sequence.

Figure out what the sequence is, then shade in the windows that should not be lit up on the final building.

b
c
FOX'S BOXES
a
b
c
e
d
All but one of these floating cubes can be made by folding the pattern.
Which cube cannot be made?

MAGICAL MEMORIES

Professor Bogglemore is looking at his old class photo from Magic School. Look at all the wizards and witches and answer the questions below.

a. How many are wearing hats?
b. How many have glasses?
c. How many are wearing a scarf?
d. How many have their eyes closed?
e. Without counting, how many people are in the photo?
f. Again, without counting them all, how many eyes must there be in total?

WANDA'S WAND

Wanda's wand has been mixed up with the others. Hers only makes star clusters that are multiples of four. Which is it?

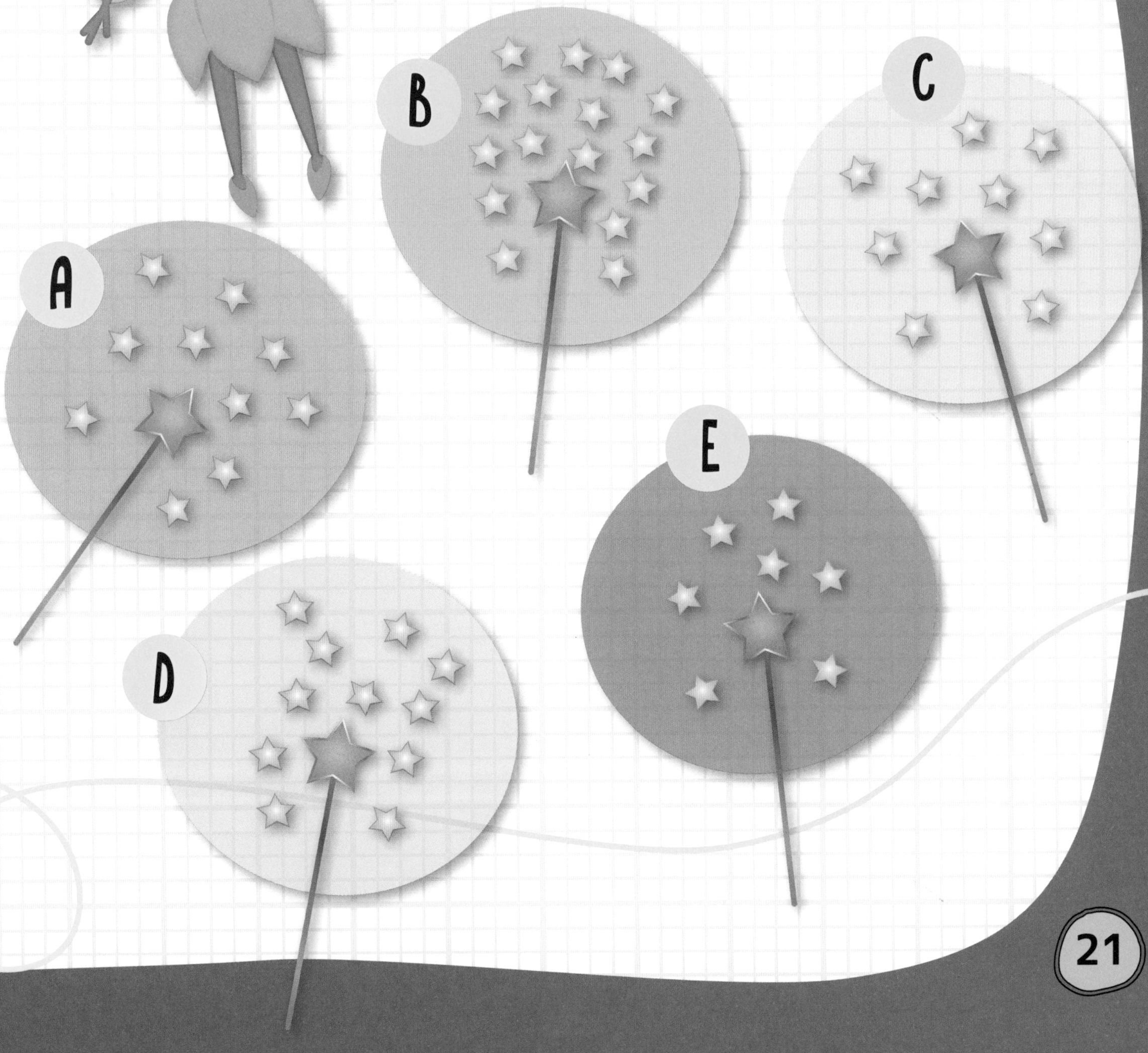

A

B

C

D

E

EYE TRICKS

Mr. Mystical has some mind-bending tricks up his sleeve. Let your mind be baffled by these amazing illusions!

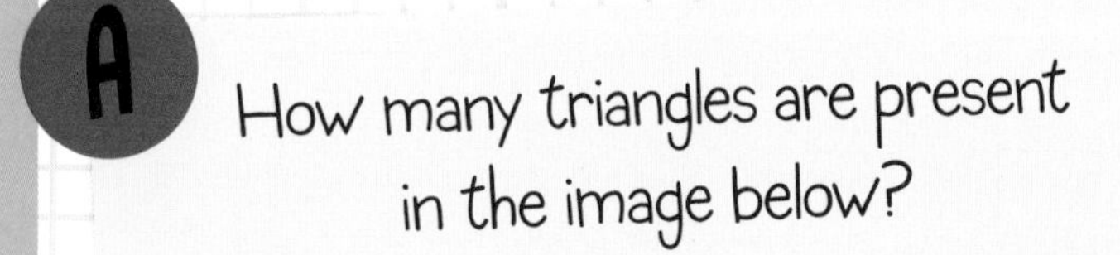

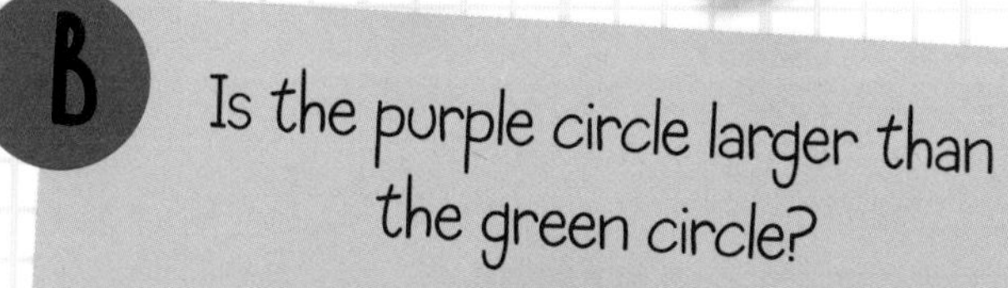

Super Sudoku

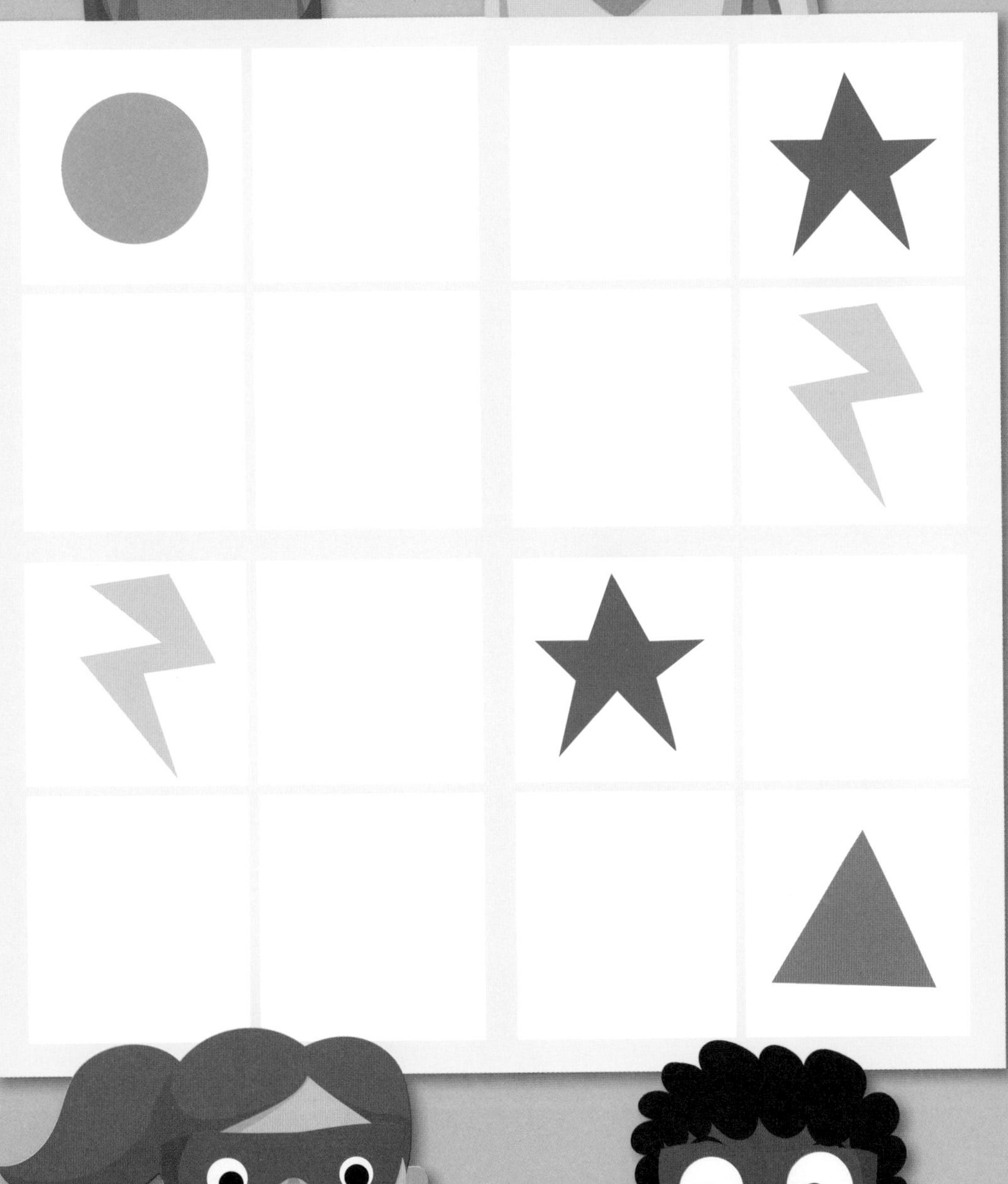

Joe Genius and his super friends each have a special super symbol.

Fill in the grid so that each row, column, and mini-grid has one of each symbol.

SOLVE IT IN SPACE

The number in the middle of each meteor is made by doing a calculation with the other smaller numbers.

Fill in the missing numbers!

A LINE IN THE STARS

Join the stars using only six straight lines, without taking your pen or pencil off the page until you've finished.

DINO SPOTTER!

Look at this Diplodocus family. Which of the dinosaurs at the bottom is the fifth family member?

Conundrum's Lair

Captain Conundrum is a supervillain who loves setting tricky puzzles. Can you solve them?

1 I go from a large room to a small room. Doors close. When the same doors open again, I can see a different large room. How is that possible?

2 I fall down my 40-step staircase, but I am unhurt. Why not?

3 I have one in every corner and two in every room. But what are they?

4 I sit at something that has four legs, but it cannot walk, and a head but it cannot talk. What is it?

PET PARADE

Amy, Sam, and Lara all belong to Pet Club. Use the clues to figure out whose pet is whose, what each pet is called, and their ages.

You can use the grid on the opposite page to keep track of everything. Fill in the blanks once you've figured it all out.

1. The girl with the ponytail has a pet with no patches.
2. The smallest pet is the oldest.
3. Sam's pet is called Patch.
4. Lara's pet's name starts with the same letter as her name.
5. Amy's pet is the youngest.
6. Patch has a brown eye patch.

	AMY	SAM	LARA
RABBIT			
DOG			
HAMSTER			
BUSTER			
LULU			
PATCH			
AGED 1			
AGED 3			
AGED 4			

Amy's pet is a _________ called _________, aged _______.

Sam's pet is a _________ called _________, aged _______.

Lara's pet is a _________ called _________, aged _______.

Egg Hunt

Look at all the chickens on the farm. Each chicken has laid six eggs. How many are hidden in the hen house?

Juggling Act

These jugglers can do an amazing trick with their juggling balls. Which new juggler could join their act?

FAMILY FUN

Ben and Bella come from a big family. Ben has as many brothers as he has sisters, but Bella has only half as many sisters as she has brothers.

How many boys and girls in total are there in the family?

TELEPHONE TEST

Ben is on the phone.

The person he is talking to is the son of his grandfather and grandmother but it's not his uncle.

Who is Ben talking to?

MAKE A WISH

Ben and his dad share the same birthday, but how old are they this year? Write their ages on the birthday cards.

CLUES

Their ages add up to 66.
Dad's age is Ben's age reversed.
Ben's age is a multiple of 5.

A SHARE OF THE KINGDOM

King Laurence wants to give part of his kingdom to his four grandchildren. They must each receive an equal, L-shaped share. How should he divide the plot of land between them?

LOTS OF LEGS!

Farmer Frank keeps chickens and pigs on his farm. There are 15 heads and 42 legs in total.

How many chickens and how many pigs does Farmer Frank have?

FAIRIES AND FIREFLIES

Wendy the Fairy keeps pet fireflies.

All but two glow red.
All but two glow purple.
All but two glow yellow.

How many fireflies
does Wendy have
altogether?

MAGIC TEST

Complete the grid so that every row, column, and mini grid includes just one of each symbol shown.

DETECTIVE DOG

Detective Dog has lost his bone at the park. Read the clues to help him find it again.

1. He left his bone next to a group of three trees.
2. He doesn't like birds. He won't go near them.
3. Dogs aren't allowed near the café.
4. He is allergic to flower pollen.

Detective Dog's bone is in location: ______________

Which Switch is Which?

Ivan the inventor has just finished his latest robot. The only problem is, he can't remember which switch will activate him...

Which switch should Ivan flip to bring his robot to life?

GAMES NIGHT

The super friends are playing a tricky dice game. The winner is the player with the highest score made by adding up the numbers they have rolled with the numbers face down on the opposite side of the dice.

Lucie

Joe

Pete

Susie

WHO HAS WON THIS ROUND?

Owl's Flower Garden

Wise Old Owl loves gardening. He needs a new watering can. Which one will hold the most water?

FLOWER POWER

Look at Owl's prize-winning flowers. Can you plant the next seven flowers for him?

THE CAMEL'S COINS

Mo and his camel have been trekking across the desert, collecting money that is owed to Mo.

The first merchant paid Mo 24 coins.

The second merchant paid him half that amount.

Mo then bought some water for his camel for 9 coins.

The third merchant paid Mo the same as the second.

The last merchant doubled the coins in the camel's pouch.

HOW MANY COINS IS MO LEFT WITH?

Pet Portraits

Buster, Patch, and Lulu have each had their portrait drawn, but the artist has made some changes to each pet's appearance! Can you spot the difference in each painting?

Buster

A DAY AT THE BEACH

It's Sunday and Sam and his friends are meeting to celebrate Sam's birthday with a trip to the seaside. Sam says:

Two days before the day before yesterday, it was my birthday!

When was Sam's birthday?

ICE CREAMS ALL ROUND!

The friends are each treating themselves to an ice cream. Look at all the delicious toppings! What toppings should the last ice cream have?

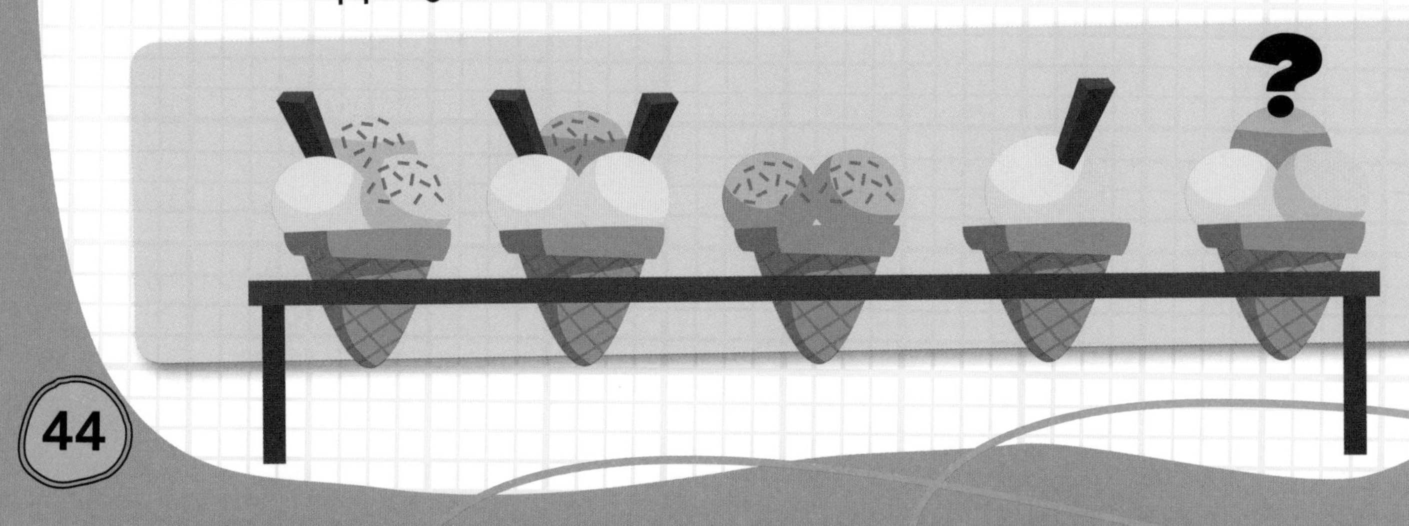

PATTERNS IN THE SAND

Sam, Amy, and Lara are making patterns in the sand. Can you join up all the starfish with one continuous line to make one big star?

FOX'S FAMILY

Fox comes from a big family! He has 3 brothers and 2 sisters and they have 25 fox cubs between them.

Fox has 5 cubs of his own.

All of his siblings have at least 2 cubs.

Two of his brothers have 6 cubs.

Both of his sisters have the same number of cubs.

One of his brothers has fewer than 3 cubs.

How many fox cubs does each sibling have?

The super friends have been making super shapes!

Super Shapes

Look at the pattern and then draw the next two rows.

ROBOT GRID

Can you find this robot's tummy display inside the main grid?

PTEROSAUR TEST

Look at all the pterosaur nests and eggs. The spots on the eggs in each nest follow the same pattern.

Figure out the sequence and draw the correct number of spots on the blank eggs.

WHAT'S COOKING?

World-famous chef, Pierre Gateaux, has a very special meal to prepare but someone has tidied the kitchen and all he can find are these two timers!

His sauce needs to simmer for 5 minutes. Will Pierre be able to accurately time his cooking? And if so, how?

Kitchen Nightmare

Three boxes have been delivered to Pierre's kitchen:
One contains cheese. One contains bread.
One contains cheese and bread.

All the boxes have been labelled incorrectly! Can you label all the boxes correctly by opening just one of the boxes?

Which box should you choose?

OWL'S RIDDLE SCHOOL

Wise Old Owl is teaching at his Riddle School. Will you be top of the class?

1. I have rings that I do not wear, but they tell you how old I am. What am I?
2. Which word contains 26 letters but only 3 syllables?
3. I'm light as a feather, yet the strongest person cannot hold me for more than 5 minutes. What am I?
4. What building has the most stories?
5. What can be seen in water but never gets wet?

BAKING ME CRAZY!

Look at these scrummy cupcakes. Which is the odd one out?

MR. MYSTICAL'S EYE TRICKS!

Stare at the image and prepare to be amazed!

A

You will see little black dots inside the white circles on the left... but are they really there?

B

Are the horizontal lines in this image straight or slanted?

At the Races

Owl and Fox are having a day out watching the snail racing. Using these clues, can you figure out the order in which the snails finished?

1. The purple snail is not the winner.
2. The yellow snail was not first or last.
3. Green finished two places behind orange.
4. Orange did not finish in second place.
5. Blue finished straight after purple.

JEWEL THIEVES

Light-Fingered Louis and Baby-Faced Bob have been at it again! This time, they've stolen some priceless jewels.

4 jewels

6 jewels

10 jewels

12 jewels

There's a pattern between the number of jewels in each bag.

A. How many jewels must there be in the final sack?

B. How many jewels have they stolen in total?

SNOOZE MODE

This robot is in snooze mode. Complete the number grid to activate her.

Z Z Z Z Z Z

4		2		5	
		4		6	
	2				3
2			5		4
		1		3	
3		6			5

Each row, column, and mini-grid must have different numbers from 1 to 6.

PIRATE PUZZLER!

Look at this swashbuckling line up. Read the clues below to identify each pirate's pet, the treasure they're seeking, and where it's hidden! You can use the grid opposite to help you.

Redbeard

Seagull Sam

Peg-Leg Meg

Scallywag

Barnacle

Jolly Roger

Gold

Gemstones

Cups & Pearls

Dead Man's Cove

Stinky Squid Island

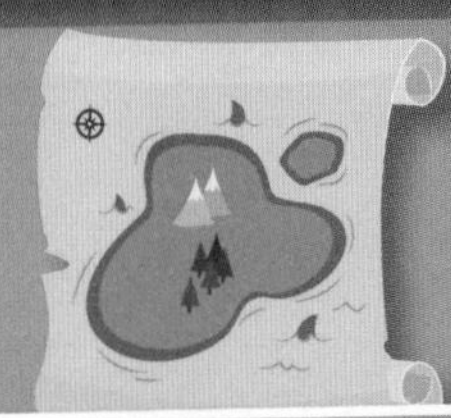

Sharkbait Bay

1. Redbeard's pet has an earring.
2. Scallywag's owner is looking for gold.
3. Peg-Leg Meg is allergic to cat fur.
4. Seagull Sam won't go to Dead Man's Cove.
5. Jolly Roger is excited to see his pals on Stinky Squid Island.
6. Dead Man's Cove is where the gemstones are hidden.

	Redbeard	Seagull Sam	Peg-Leg Meg
Scallywag			
Barnacle			
Jolly Roger			
Gold			
Gemstones			
Cups & Pearls			
Dead Man's Cove			
Stinky Squid Island			
Sharkbait Bay			

Redbeard's pet is _______. He is looking for the _______, hidden at _______.

Seagull Sam's pet is _______. He is looking for the _______, hidden at _______.

Peg-Leg Meg's pet is _______. She is looking for the _______, hidden at _______.

MORE MIND-BENDING MATCHSTICKS!

Change three matchsticks into six without breaking them apart.

Make this sum correct by moving only one matchstick.

Mirror, Mirror

Princess Susannah has a magical mirror. Sometimes it plays tricks with reflections! Which image matches the reflection of the princess?

A

B

C

CHESS TOURNAMENT

Ben and Bella have entered the chess tournament at school. There are 13 other children taking part, and anyone who loses a match is out of the competition.

How many matches must be played before they crown the Chess Champion?

SEASIDE SHUFFLE

Which three creatures come next, a, b, or c?

Odd Bug Out
Owl has been looking after these spotty bugs. Every bug has a matching partner, apart from one. Can you spot the odd bug out?

WRONG TURN

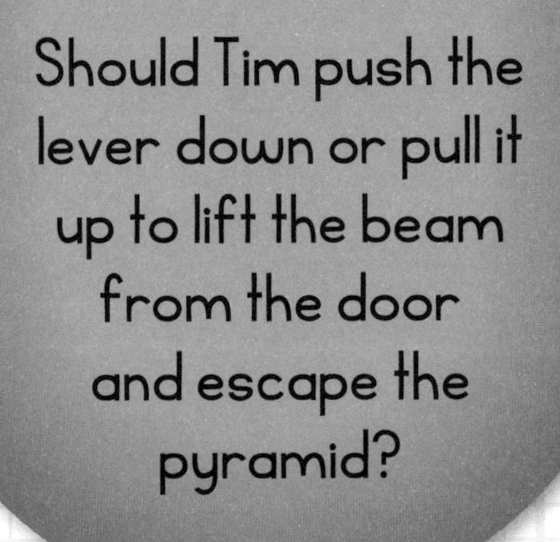

Should Tim push the lever down or pull it up to lift the beam from the door and escape the pyramid?

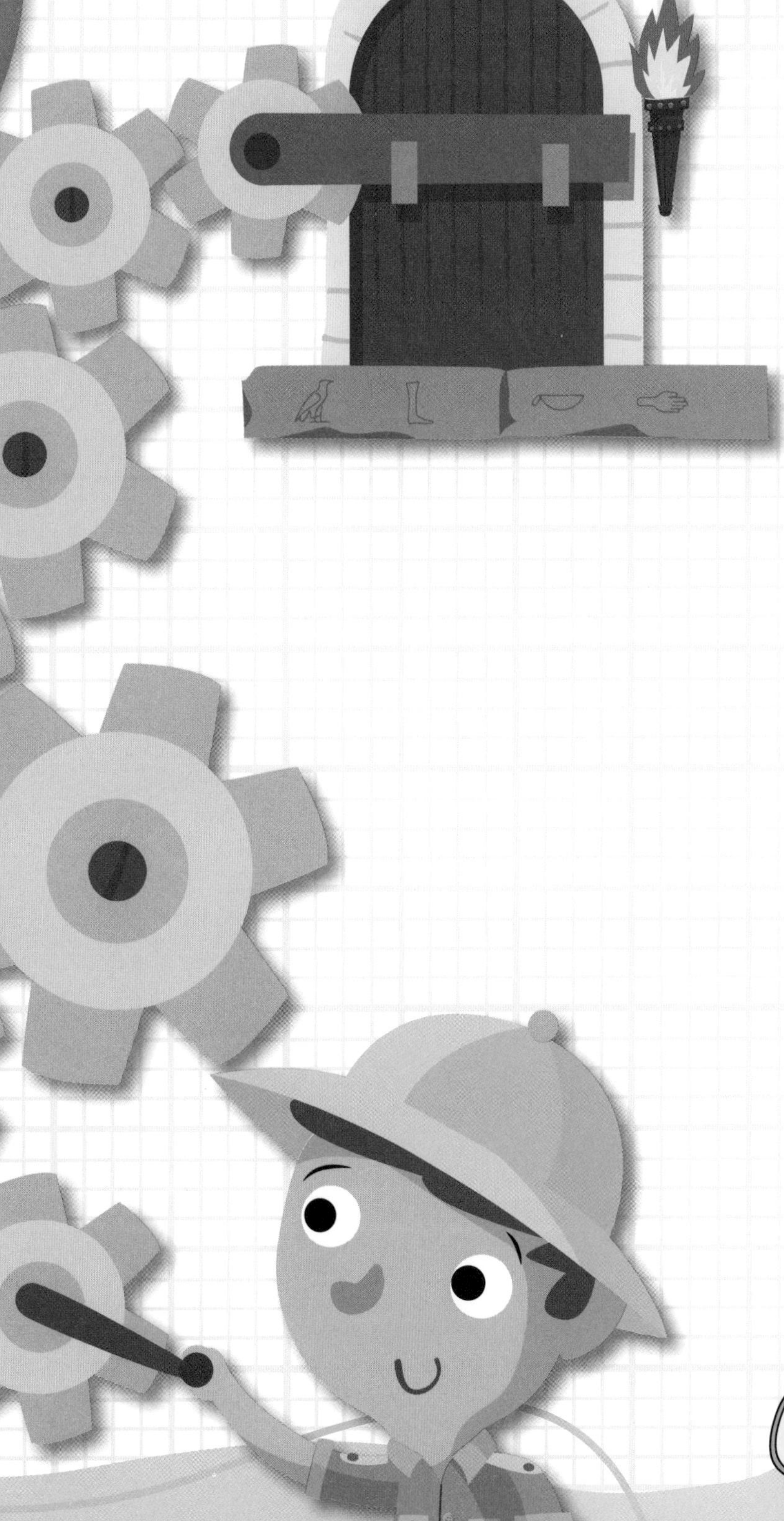

MAD SCIENCE

Ivan's been working in his lab all day. He's trying to create a potion to boost brain power!

He's lining up his ingredients in preparation. Which two bottles come next?

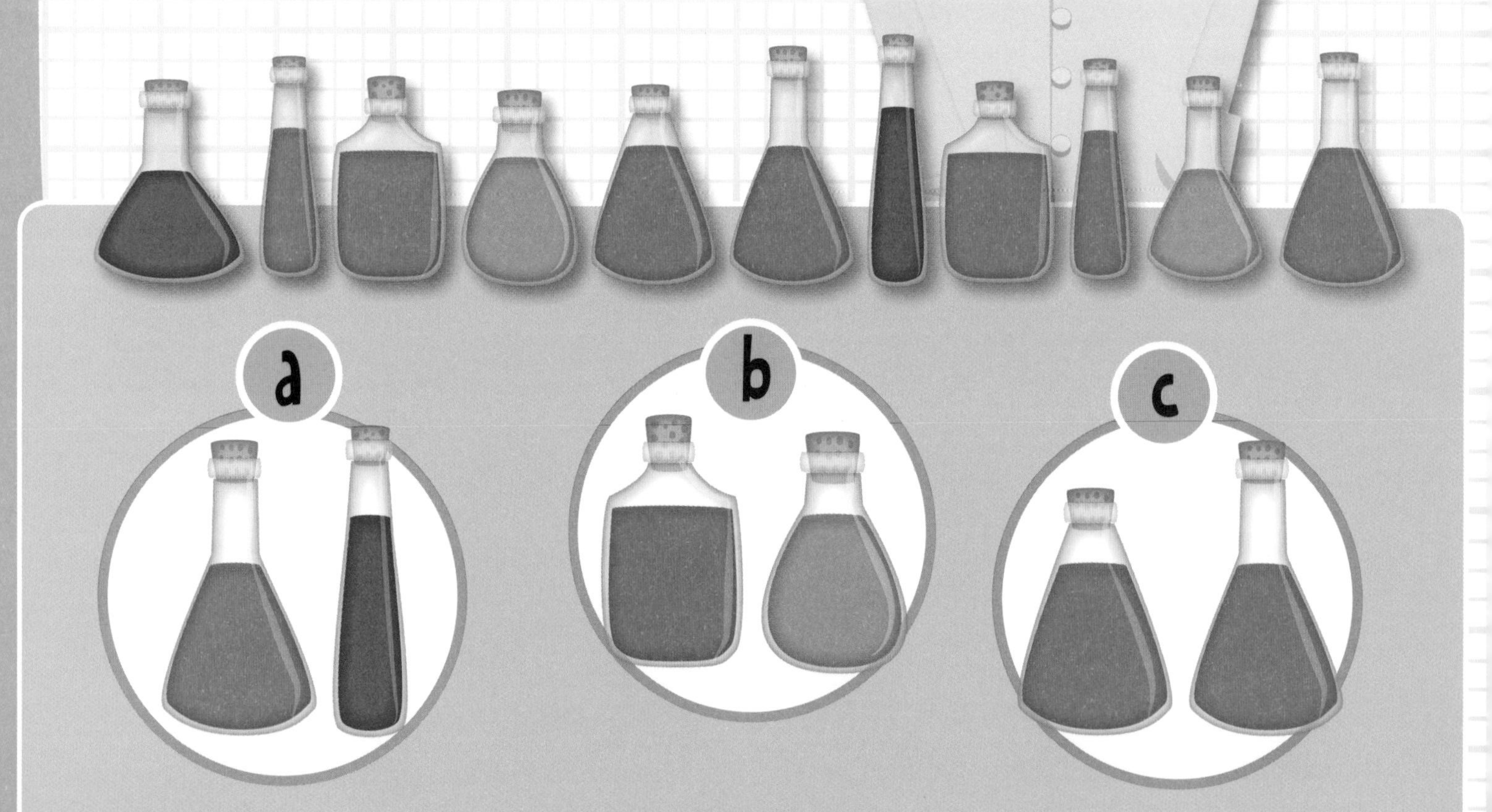

Wanda's training her brain by completing this picture grid. Fill in the grid so that each row, column, and mini-grid has one of each symbol.

PROBLEM PETS

The pets are lining up to go for a walk. The problem is, some of them are very fussy... Put the pets in the right order for their walk.

Patch has to be the leader.

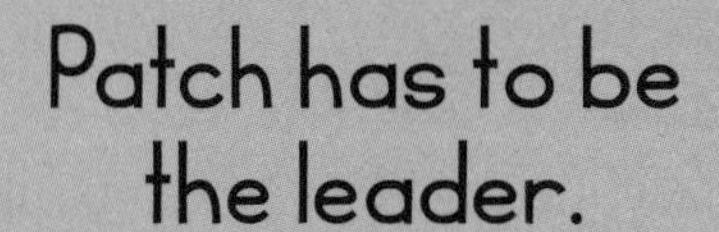

Larry likes to be next to Fifi.

Fifi has to go right after Lulu.

Buster won't go last.

Larry

Bogglemore's Books

Which is Professor Bogglemore's missing book, a, b, or c?

a

b
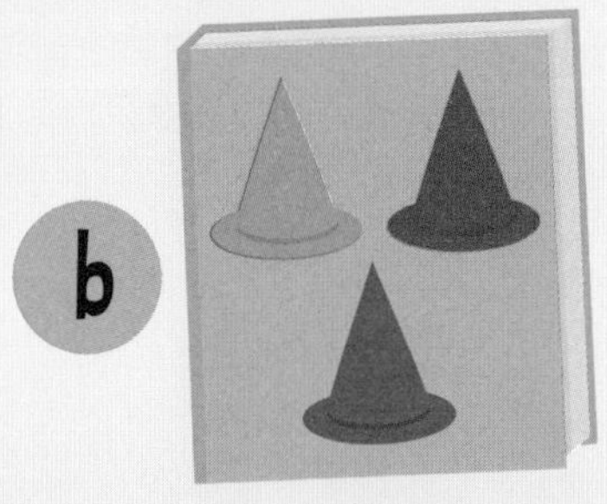
c
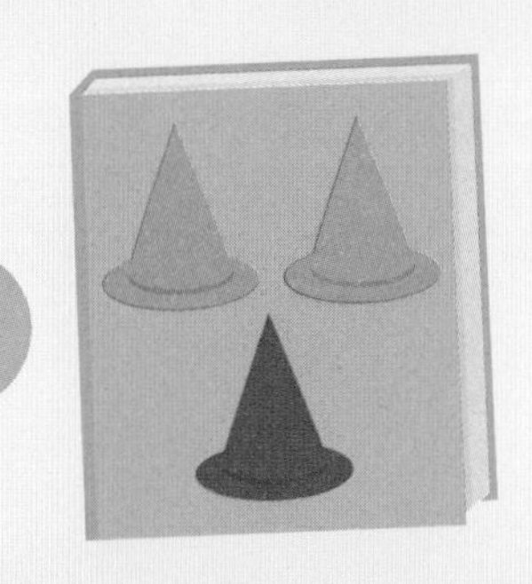

ASTRO-GRID

Guide the astronaut through space, following the objects in the order shown below. You can move up, down, and across, but not diagonally.

1 2 3

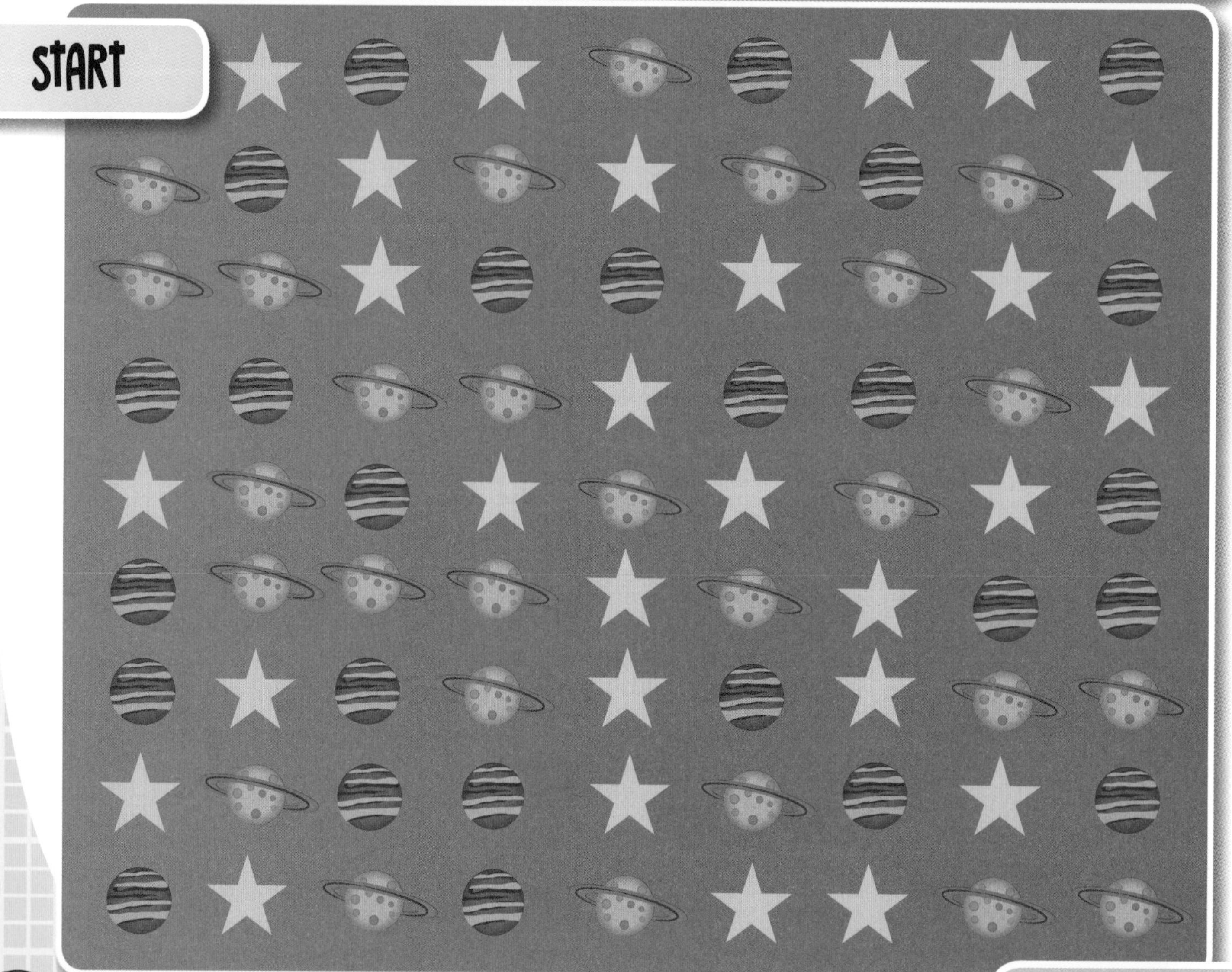

FINISH

Super-Dancing Skills

The super friends have taken part in a dance competition. The competitors' moves are marked out of a possible 50 points. What were their scores and who won?

Joe Genius

CLUES

Joe Genius scored 44 out of 50.

Susie Superstar scored 7 points more than Lucie.

Puzzler Pete scored half that of Susie.

Lightning Lucie scored 76% of the maximum. possible score.

Lightning Lucie

Susie Superstar

Joe scored: ____ points

Susie scored: ____ points

Pete scored: ____ points

Lucie scored: ____ points

Puzzler Pete

The Getaway Gang

The thieving gang has stolen a priceless painting! They're on the run in their getaway car.

They drive 100 miles to the drop-off point at 100 miles per hour. They get stuck in traffic on the way back to their secret base and only average 25 miles per hour for the 100-mile journey back.

What was their average speed for the whole getaway?

NUMBER CRUNCHER

These machines all MULTIPLY by a number and then ADD a different number. They all do the same thing.

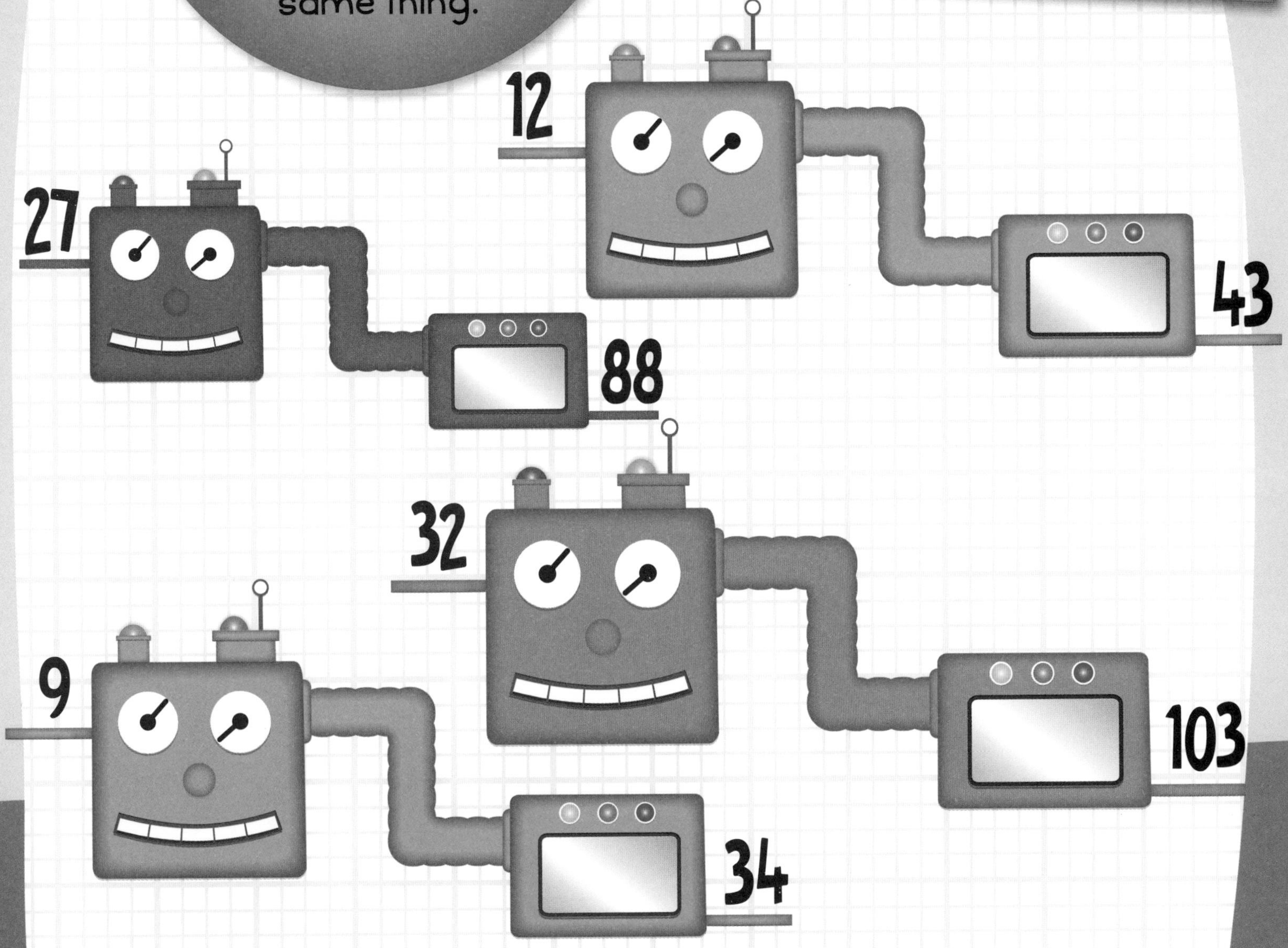

12 → 43

27 → 88

32 → 103

9 → 34

What would happen to these numbers if they entered any one of the machines?

A 15 B 30 C 53

SAM AND SCALLYWAG

Sam and Scallywag have been out treasure hunting all day.

At Sharkbait Bay they find 375 gold coins.

At Rattlebone River they find double that number.

They lose a bet to Peg Leg Meg in Timber Inn and hand over one third of their haul to her.

At Sinker Point they lose 75 coins to a rival ship.

Finally, at Baracuda Bay they plunder three dozen rubies, each worth 13 gold coins.

Once they have sold all the rubies, how much will Sam and Scallywag be left with?

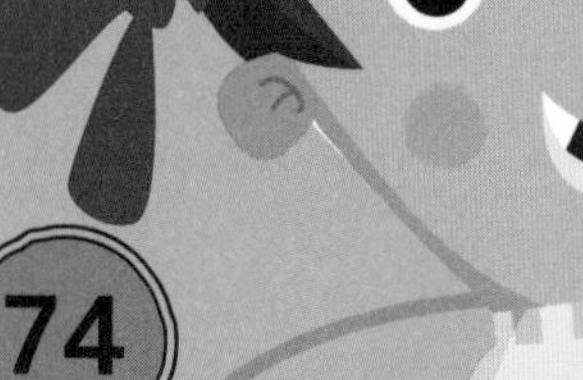

BAD KNIGHT

The knights have all assembled to greet the king. But there is a bad knight amongst them, spying on them for a rival kingdom! The spy lost an ear in battle—can you spot him?

THE LIGHT BULB TRICK

Follow Mr. Mystical's instructions and you won't believe your eyes...

Robot Grids

Find each robot's tummy display inside the main grid.

PYRAMID PUZZLE

Figure out the number pattern on the pyramid and fill in the missing blocks. Is the top number higher or lower than 500?

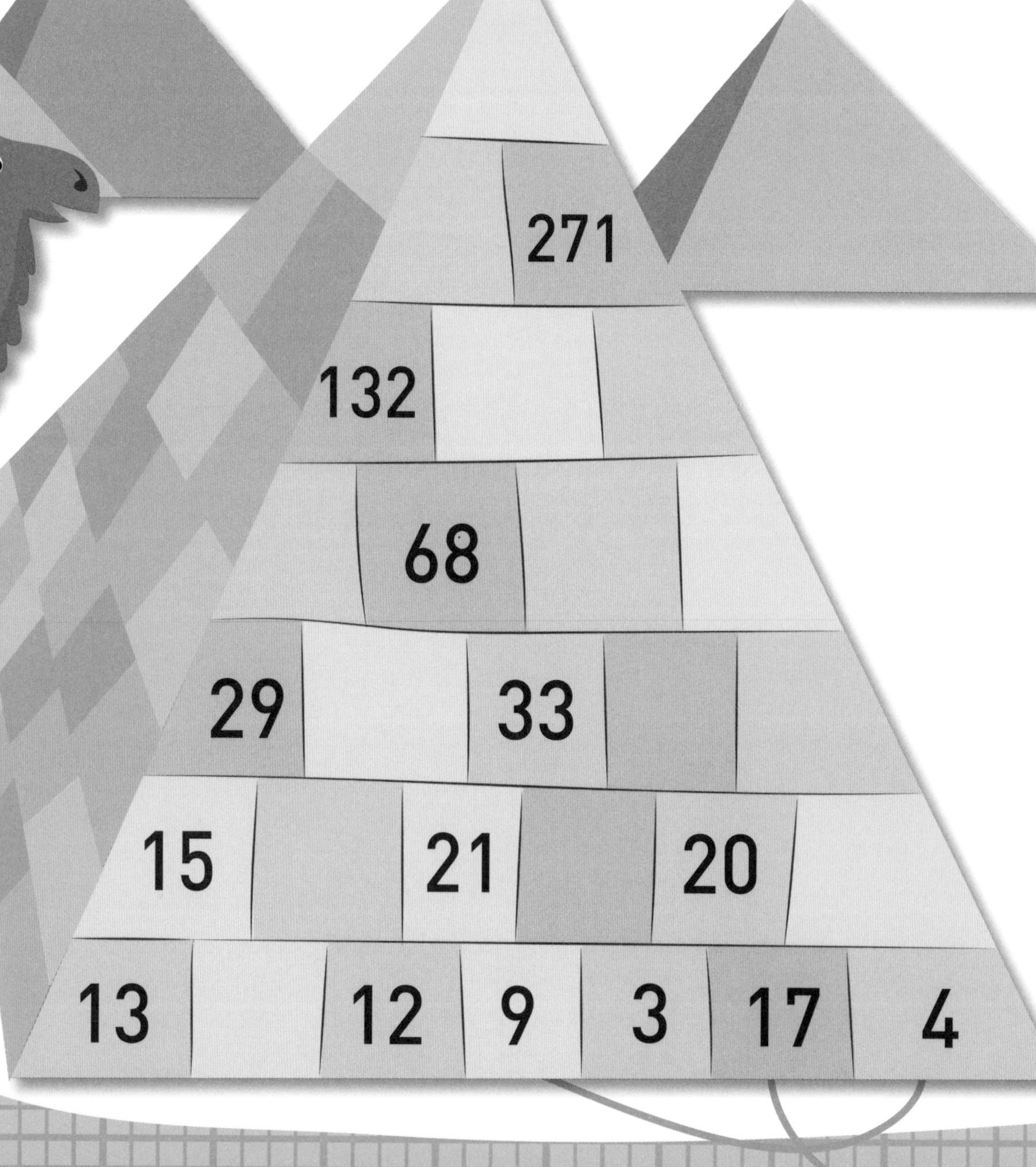

FUNNY FISH

Look at the two aquariums.

Which fish belongs in tank 1? Which fish belongs in tank 2?

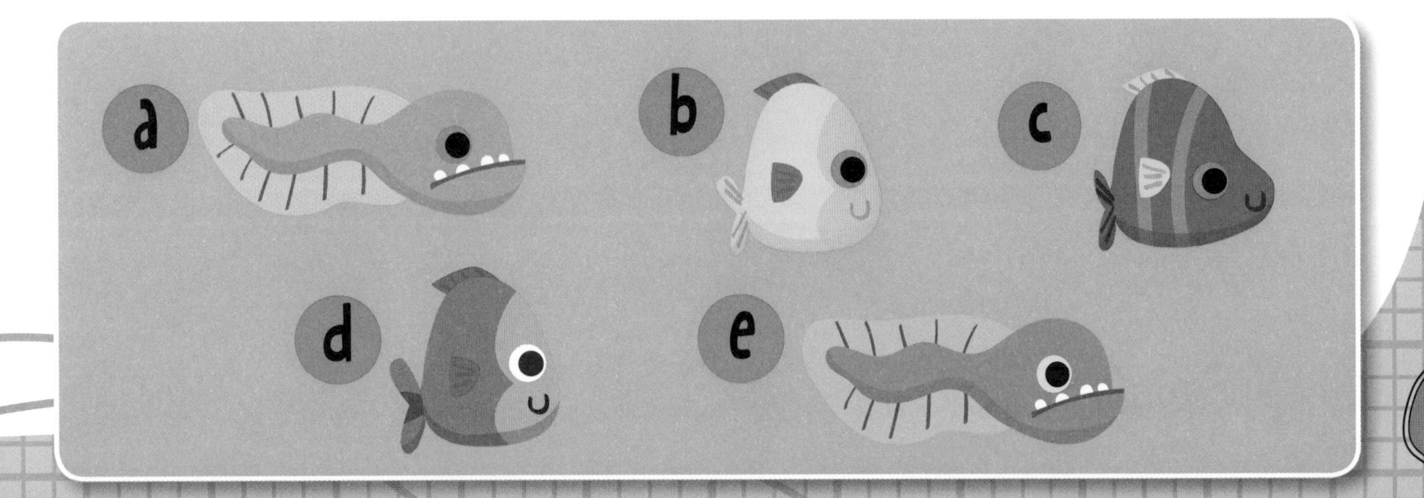

DINNER TIME

Pierre Gateaux is in the kitchen preparing dinner for the hungry customers in his restaurant. Pierre's food is delicious, but he can only cook one dish at a time!

Look at the menu and cooking times opposite and answer the following questions. Diners must always choose one starter, one main, and one dessert.

1. Marco on table 4 is really hungry. Which starter, main, and dessert should he order to get served in the fastest time possible?

   How long will that take Pierre to cook?
2. Which starter, main, and dessert combination will take Pierre exactly 2 hours to cook?
3. Which starter, main, and dessert combination takes the longest cooking time?

   How long will that take Pierre to cook?
4. Which menu combinations both take exactly 3 hours and 20 minutes to cook?
5. How many starter, main, and dessert combinations are there in total?

STARTERS

French onion soup

Cooking time: 55 mins

Cheese soufflé

Cooking time: 40 mins

Baked snails

Cooking time: 35 mins

MAINS

Tomato tart

Cooking time: 1hr25 mins

Mussels and fries

Cooking time: 30 mins

Lobster

Cooking time: 40 mins

DESSERTS

Chocolate cake

Cooking time: 1hr15 mins

Crepes

Cooking time: 35 mins

Lemon tart

Cooking time: 1hr45 mins

FARM MIX-UP

Farmer Frank wants to put the chickens and pigs back in the right pens. Only swapping one chicken with one pig at a time, how many swaps will it take to move them all around?

Gone Fishing

Friends Amy, Sam, and Lara have gone on a fishing trip. None of them are having much luck catching fish...

Each of the super friends likes a different super food! Read the clues to work out who likes what best.

Kale

Strawberries

Avocado

Apple

Blueberries

Broccoli

Pumpkin

Almonds

A The food Pete likes is orange and green.

B Lucie hates green vegetables. Her food starts with the letter B.

C No one likes avocado best.

D The berry Susie likes has seeds.

E The food Joe likes has pips.

Pete likes ______________________________

Susie likes ______________________________

Lucie likes ______________________________

Joe likes ______________________________

Unlock the Vault

Baby-Faced Bob might be small, but he's smart! Is he clever enough to crack the code that unlocks the vault?

	3	9	2		5	7	6	
5		1	9				2	
2				7	8			9
3		5	7	6		4		
7		6			1			5
4		8	5	3		9	7	
9		7	6	2		5		1
	5	3	8					
	8	2			4	3	9	

To open the vault, fill in the grid so that each row, column, and mini-grid has one of each number from 1 to 9.

Captain Conundrum loves to boggle your brain with his ridiculous riddles. Are you brainy enough to face up to him?

CAPTAIN CONUNDRUM'S RIDDLES

1. When I start with five and add six, I get eleven, but when I start with six and add seven I get one. What am I?
2. I always ask but never answer, what am I?
3. I hold water but I am full of holes, what am I?
4. I can burst through glass without breaking it, what am I?
5. You cannot see me without light but I am always dark, what am I?

HAUNTED HOTEL

Detective Dog has been called to a hotel. Three different ghosts have been seen by the staff – it's haunted!

They are all in shock and their memories are fuzzy. Read the clues to help Detective Dog figure out who saw which ghost and where!

Molly

Giles

Trevor

Green ghost

Ghost dog

Lady of the Manor

Bathroom

Entrance hall

Bedroom

1. Molly has seen the green ghost before, but not this time.
2. Trevor never goes into the hotel bedrooms.
3. The ghost Giles saw was heard barking.
4. The Lady of the Manor doesn't haunt the entrance hall.
5. The ghost dog only haunts places with running water.

	Molly the Maid	Giles the Butler	Trevor the Gardener
GREEN GHOST			
GHOST DOG			
LADY OF THE MANOR			
BATHROOM			
ENTRANCE HALL			
BEDROOM			

Molly the Maid saw ____________ in the ______________.

Giles the Butler saw __________ in the ______________.

Trevor the Gardener saw __________ in the ______________.

Answers

4. Wise Old Owl's Library

With each set of books, you add the number of icons on the first two book covers to make the total on the third.

5. Robots Rule!

The robots multiply by 4.
The green robot: 48.
The red robot: 9.

6. Breakfast Brain Training

7. The Odd Alien

F.

8. Key to the Kingdom

Shifting Shields

The shades rotate in a clockwise direction.

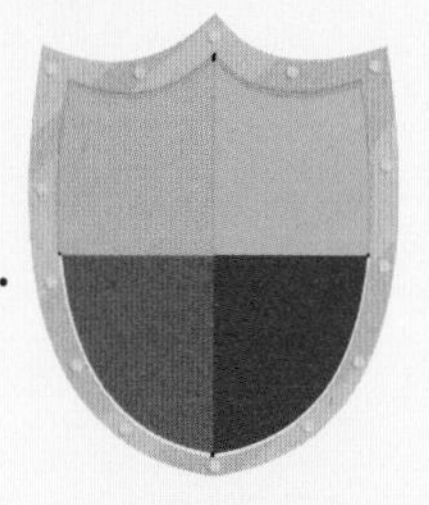

9. Double Trouble

59 MINUTES. The frogs double every minute. The box would have been half full one minute before it became completely full. Between minute 59 and minute 60 the frogs doubled their space and the box went from half full to full.

10. The Wild West

Giddy-Up Gill lives above the Store.
Curly. Pete lives above the Bank.
Bronco Bill lives above the Saloon.
Cactus Jack lives above the Sheriff.

11. Cactus Jack's Trip

Cactus Jack's horse is called Friday!

12. What to Wear?

Captain Cutlass should wear:
D: Pirate boots. E: Ruffle shirt.

13. Mind-bending Matchsticks

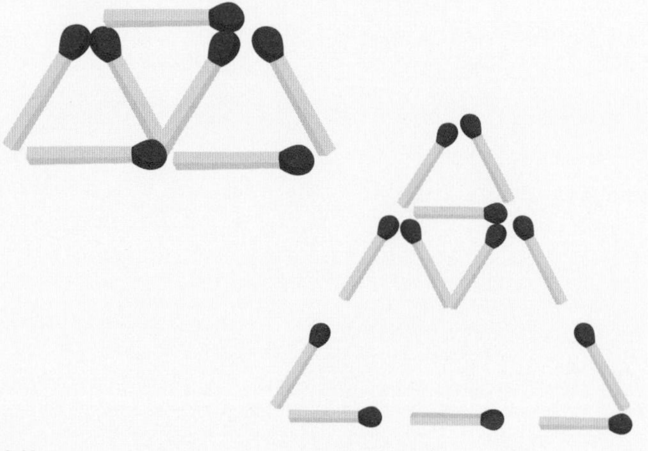

(Other solutions are possible.)

14. Pyramid Puzzle

Calculate the number above by adding the two numbers immediately below it.

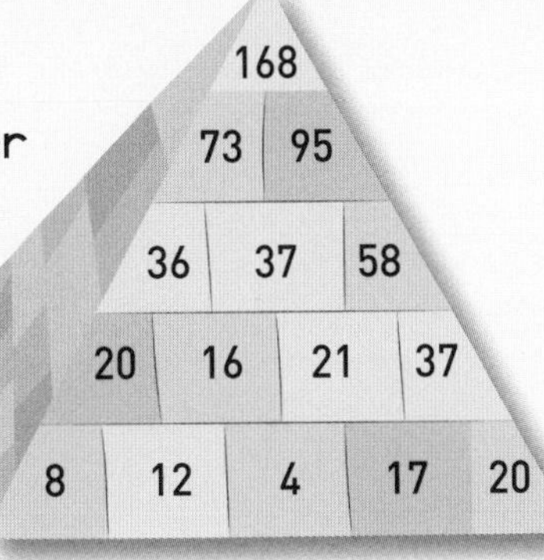

15. Pharaoh's Secret

THIS TOMB IS EMPTY.

16. Time to Run!

B.

17. Split it!

Burglar Bea gets 30 bars.
Light-Fingered Louis gets 6 bars.
Robber Rick gets 15 bars.
Baby-Faced Bob gets 9 bars.

18. Night Shift

The last building should have 15 windows lit up. In each set of 3 buildings, the formula is: Number of lit windows in building 1 x number of lit windows in building 2 = number of lit windows in building 3.

19. Fox's Boxes

D.

20. Magical Memories

(a) 12 are wearing hats.
(b) 5 have glasses.
(c) 6 are wearing a scarf.
(d) 8 have their eyes closed.
(e) There are 25 people in the photo.
(f) There are 50 eyes in total.

21. Wanda's Wand

Wand B is Wanda's, because there are 16 stars.

22. Eye Tricks

A. There aren't any triangles. There are only three V-shapes and three shapes that look like a cake with a missing piece.
B. No, they are the same size!

23. Super Sudoku

24. Solve it in Space

A: 12 B: 8. To work it out, add the number on the left to the number in the top middle. Then divide the result by the number on the right.

25. A Line in the Stars

(Other solutions are possible.)

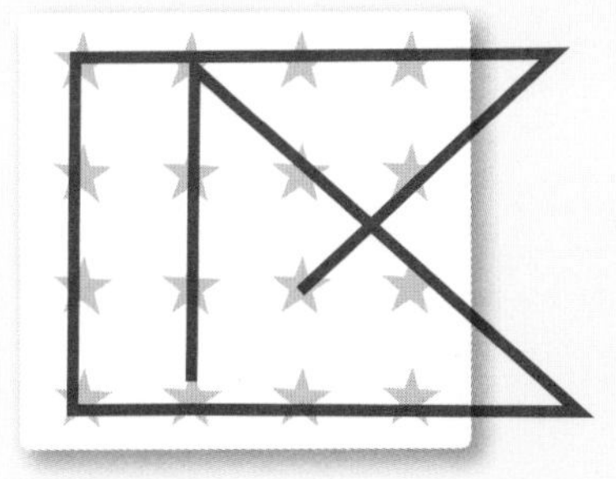

26. Dino Spotter!

D.

27. Conundrum's Lair

(1) He's in a elevator.
(2) He falls off the bottom step.
(3) The letter "o".
(4) A table.

29. Pet Parade
Amy's pet is a rabbit called Buster, aged 1.
Sam's pet is a dog called Patch, aged 3
Lara's pet is a hamster called Lulu, aged 4.

30. Egg Hunt
5 chickens x 6 eggs = 30 eggs.
There must be 6 eggs in the hen house.

31. Juggling Act
The middle number is the sum of the outer two numbers.
The answer is Juggler B.

32. Family Fun
There are four boys and three girls.

Telephone Test
Ben is on the phone to his dad.

33. Make a Wish!
Ben is 15.
Ben's dad is 51.

34 A Share of the Kingdom

35. Lots of Legs!
Both animals have at least two legs, so 15 heads must mean 30 x legs. The remaining 12 legs must belong to the pigs, which have two more legs than chickens, giving Frank:
6 pigs, with 24 legs in total.
9 chickens, with 18 legs in total.

36. Fairies and Fireflies
2 do not glow red, 1 does glow red.
2 do not glow purple, 1 does glow purple.
2 do not glow yellow, 1 does glow yellow
This adds up to 3 fireflies, 1 red, 1 purple, and 1 yellow.

37. Magic Test

38. Detective Dog
Detective Dog's bone is in location C.

39. Which Switch is Which?
Switch B.

40. Games Night
No one has won, they all scored 14.
The opposite faces of a dice always add up to 7.

41. Owl's Flower Garden
B: The shorter can with the longer spout.

This watering can's spout is taller than its rim, allowing it to be filled to the top without overflowing. The other one will overflow if you fill it above spout level, so it can hold less water even though it looks bigger!

41. Flower Power

You should have drawn 7 little yellow flowers. In between each of the large purple flowers, the number of small flowers increases by one each time.

42. The Camel's Coins

Mo is left with 78 coins.

43. Pet Portraits

44. A Day at the Beach

Sam's birthday was on Wednesday.

Ice Creams All Round!

Vanilla ice cream always has a chocolate flake.
Mint green ice cream always has pink sprinkles.
Strawberry ice cream always has blue sprinkles.

45. Patterns in the Sand

(Other solutions are possible.)

46. Fox's Family

Fox has 5 cubs.
Brother 1 has 6 cubs.
Brother 2 has 6 cubs.
Brother 3 has 2 cubs.
Sister 1 has 3 cubs.
Sister 2 has 3 cubs.

47. Super Shapes

In each row, the icons display in the pattern: 3, 2, 4, 2.
Each type of icon moves one space to the rightas you move down the rows.

48. Robot Grid

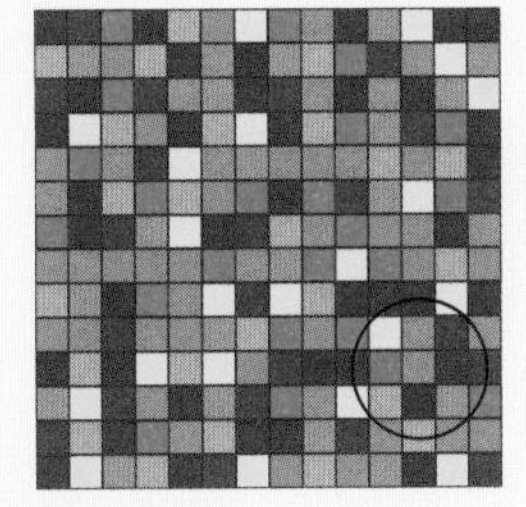

49. Pterosaur Test

The number of spots on the eggs in each nest increases as part of a times table.
A: 9 spots (3 times table).
B: 18 spots (6 times table).

50. What's Cooking?

Yes, Pierre can do it. To time 5 minutes: Flip both timers at the same time to start. When the 3-minute timer ends, quickly turn it over until the 4-minute timer ends. Then, turn the 3-minute timer over again to measure the 1 remaining minute.

51. Kitchen Nightmare

Open the box marked "cheese and bread". If it contains cheese, then you know that the box should be marked "cheese". Remember, ALL THE BOXES ARE MARKED INCORRECTLY. This means the box marked "bread" should be marked "cheese and bread", and the box marked "cheese" should be marked "bread". If the box marked "cheese and bread" contains bread, then the one marked "cheese" should be marked "cheese and bread", and the one marked "bread" should be marked "cheese".

52. Owl's Riddle School

1. A tree.
2. Alphabet.
3. Breath.
4. A library.
5. A reflection.

53. Baking Me Crazy!

Sprinkles always have a green case Choc chips always have a blue case.

54. Mr Mystical's Eye tricks!

A: The little black dots aren't really there at all! Your eyes are tricking you!

B: The horizontal lines are perfectly straight!

55. At the Races

1. Orange
2. Yellow
3. Green
4. Purple
5. Blue

56 Jewel Thieves

The number of jewels in each sack goes: + 2, + 4, + 2, + 4 and so on.

A. The last bag contains 18 jewels.

B. They have stolen 66 jewels in total.

57. Snooze Mode

4	3	2	6	5	1
1	5	4	3	6	2
6	2	5	1	4	3
2	6	3	5	1	4
5	4	1	2	3	6
3	1	6	4	2	5

58-59. Pirate Puzzler!

Redbeard's pet is Jolly Roger. He is looking for the cups and pearls hidden at Stinky Squid Island.

Seagull Sam's pet is Scallywag. He is looking for the gold hidden at Sharkbait Bay.

Peg-Leg Meg's pet is Barnacle. She is looking for the gemstones hidden at Dead Man's Cove.

60. More Mind-Bending Matchsticks!

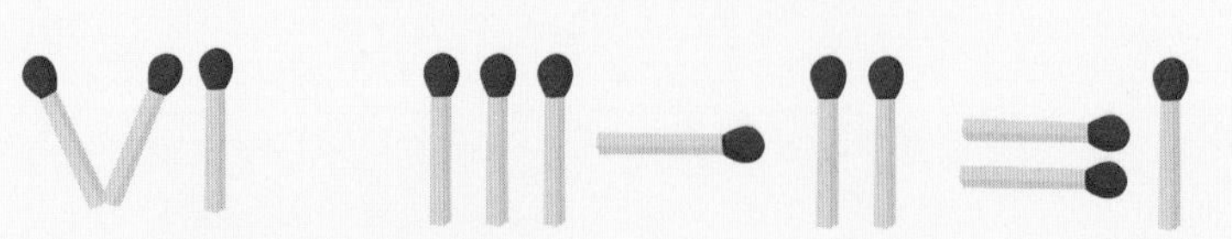

61. Mirror, Mirror

C.

62. Chess Tournament

14 matches. There are 15 children taking part. Each player apart from the winner will lose once and only once, so 15 children = 14 losers and therefore 14 matches.

63. Seaside Shuffle

B–pink shell, orange crab, purple starfish. The creatures stay in the same order (left to right), with the last creature becoming the first creature on the next line down.

64. Odd Bug Out

65. Wrong Turn

He should push it down.

66. Mad Science

A–The sequence is Red, Blue, Blue, Green, Blue, Blue, repeated.

67. Wanda's Workout

68. Problem Pets

(1) Patch. (2) Buster. (3) Lulu .(4) Fifi. (5) Larry.

69. Bogglemore's Books

B–Blue, Purple, Red. The shade of the cover images rotates clockwise by one place each time.

70. Astro-grid

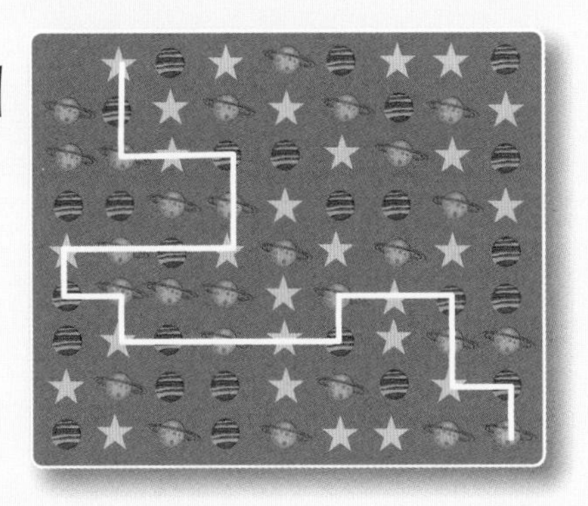

71. Super-Dancing Skills

Joe scored: 44 points.
Susie scored: 45 points.
Pete scored: 22.5 points.
Lucie scored: 38 points.

72. The Getaway Gang

It takes them 1 hour to drive the first 100 miles. It takes them 4 hours to drive the 100 miles back. So they drive a total of 200 miles in 5 hours, averaging 40 miles per hour.

73. Number Cruncher

The machine first multiplies by 3 then adds 7:
(a) 52. (b) 97. (c) 166.

74. Sam and Scallywag

375 + 750 - 375 - 75 + 468 = 1143.
Sam and Scallywag are left with 1143 gold coins.

75. Bad Knight

76. The Light Bulb Trick

You should see a glowing light bulb!

77. Robot Grids

78. Pyramid Puzzle

Yes, the top answer is 536.

536
265 271
132 133 138
64 68 65 73
29 35 33 32 41
15 14 21 12 20 21
13 2 12 9 3 17 4

79. Funny Fish

Fish E belongs in tank 1, as each fish has yellow eyes. Fish D belongs in tank 2, as each fish has a purple stripe on its tail.

80. Dinner Time

(1) Snails + Mussels + Crepes = 1hr 40 minutes.
(2) Soup + Mussels + Crepes = 2 hours.
(3) Soup + Tart + Tart = 4 hours 5 minutes.
(4) Soup + Lobster + Tart = 3 hours and 20 minutes. Souffle + Tart + Cake = 3 hours and 20 minutes.
(5) There are 27 possible combinations.

82. Farm Mix-Up

5 swaps.

83. Gone Fishing

Amy has caught a crab's claw.
Sam has caught an old boot.
Lara has caught a treasure chest.

85. Super Food

Pete likes pumpkin.
Susie likes strawberries.
Lucie likes blueberries.
Joe likes apple.

86. Unlock the Vault

8	3	9	2	1	5	7	6	4
5	7	1	9	4	6	8	2	3
2	6	4	3	7	8	1	5	9
3	2	5	7	6	9	4	1	8
7	9	6	4	8	1	2	3	5
4	1	8	5	3	2	9	7	6
9	4	7	6	2	3	5	8	1
1	5	3	8	9	7	6	4	2
6	8	2	1	5	4	3	9	7

87. Captain Conundrum's Riddles

(1) A clock. (2) A question.
(3) A sponge. (4) Light.
(5) A shadow.

89. Haunted Hotel

Molly the Maid saw the Lady of the Manor in the bedroom.
Giles the Butler saw the Ghost Dog in the bathroom.
Trevor the Gardener saw the Green Ghost in the entrance hall.